Kipper's Weather Week

Written by Annemarie Young
and illustrated by Nick Schon,
based on the original characters
created by Roderick Hunt and Alex Brychta

OXFORD
UNIVERSITY PRESS

Kipper's Weather Chart

Day [Monday] Date [27]

Month [October] Weather

Season [Autumn] Sunny Windy

Days	Weather
Monday	
Tuesday	
Wednesday	
Thursday	
Friday	
Saturday	
Sunday	

Monday was sunny and dry, but a
bit windy. Kipper found some sticks
and planks. He wanted to make a
den in the garden.

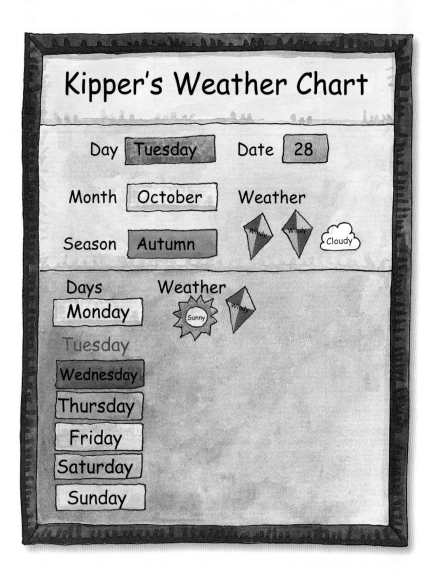

Tuesday was cloudy and very
windy. Kipper used a big cardboard
box to make a roof for his den, but
the wind kept blowing it off.

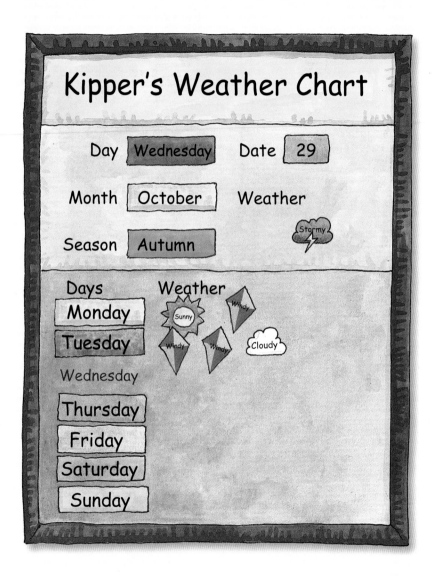

On Wednesday afternoon, there
was a thunderstorm. Kipper and
Floppy watched from inside the
house. The den got very wet!

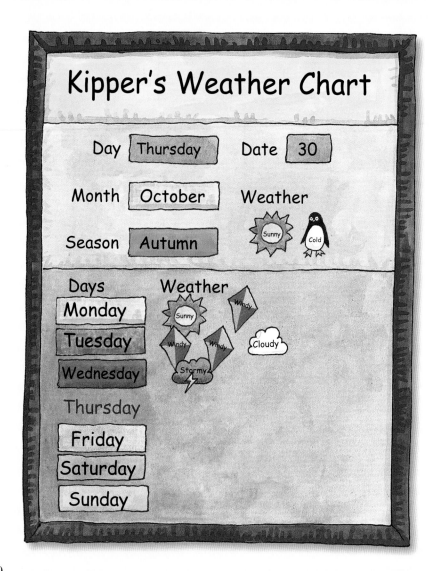

Kipper's Weather Chart

Day [Thursday]   Date [30]

Month [October]   Weather

Season [Autumn]   Sunny   Cold

Days   Weather
Monday   Sunny   Windy
Tuesday   Windy   Windy   Cloudy
Wednesday   Stormy
Thursday
Friday
Saturday
Sunday

On Thursday it was clear and
sunny, but chilly. Kipper threw away
the soggy roof. He used an old sheet
instead.

On Friday, it was foggy and a bit
gloomy. Kipper put a blanket, some
cushions and a torch in the den.
Then Floppy chased a cat. Oh no!

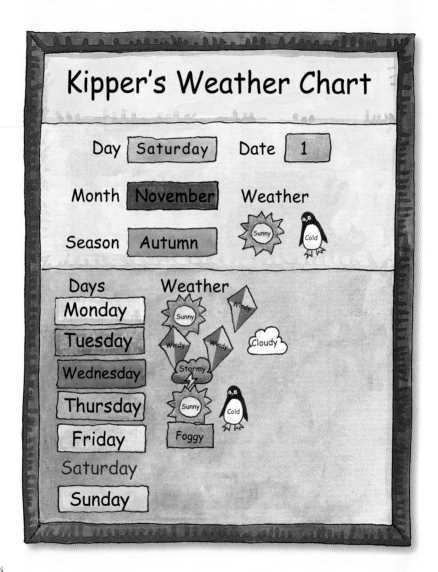

Saturday was fine, sunny and cold.
Kipper put the den back together.
Then Dad put a big sheet of plastic
over the top.

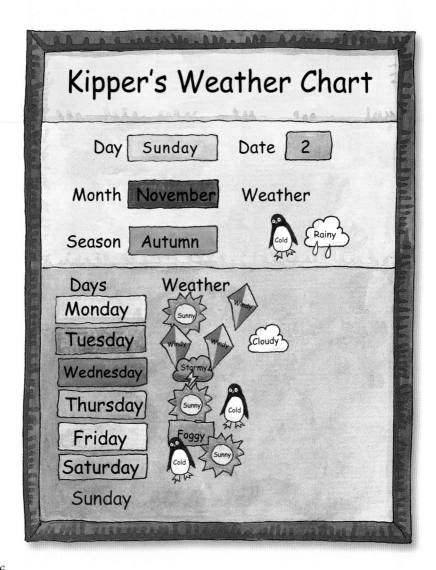

On Sunday it was raining, but it was dry inside the den. Kipper, Anna and Sam had a picnic, and Floppy came too!

Talk about the weather

What was Kipper making in the garden? What season was it?

What was the weather like on Tuesday? What happened?

Why did Kipper and Floppy stay inside on Wednesday?

Which season do you like best?

Matching

Look back at the story. Match the weather to the day.

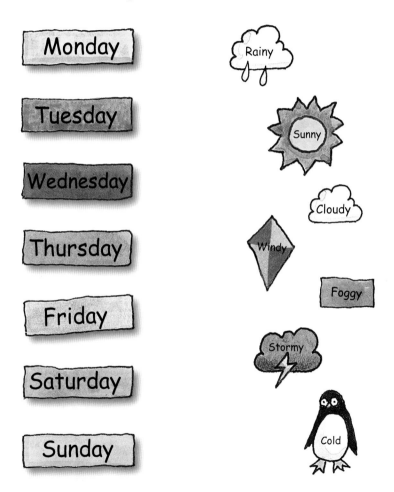

The seasons

In **winter** it is cold and sometimes it snows. We can often wake up to find frost and ice on the ground.

In **spring** the days get warmer, but the weather can change and sometimes it's cold enough to snow. It's often very windy.

In **summer** it can be hot and sunny, but it rains sometimes too. You need to protect your skin so you don't get sunburned.

In **autumn** the weather gets cooler. There are often strong winds, rain, fog and mist. It can be quite warm during the day but chilly at night.

Winter

Spring

Summer

Autumn

Weather words

Which kind of weather do you get in each of the seasons?

sunny

cloudy

windy

rainy

foggy

snowy

stormy

frosty

misty

hot

cold

warm

Kipper's weather

Match the weather symbols to what Kipper is doing.

Sunny

Foggy

Cold

Stormy

Rainy

Windy

Cloudy